Scholastic CLIFFORD THE BIG RED DOG

Phonics Reading Program — Book 12: oi, oy

Clifford's Coin

by Donna Taylor

Illustrated by Bob Roper

Based on the books by Norman Bridwell

SCHOLASTIC INC.
New York Toronto London Auckland Sydney
Mexico City New Delhi Hong Kong Buenos Aires

Dogs like to dig up soil. And that's just what Clifford was doing. He found an old shoe and an old glove. Then he dug up something shiny. It was an old coin. He was rolling it around when T-Bone came by.

T-Bone pointed to the coin. "Would you like to trade that coin for my new toy?" he asked. "It squeaks when you bite it."

"Sure," said Clifford. And the trade was made.

Clifford ran off with his squeaky toy and T-Bone started rolling his coin.

Then Cleo came by. She pointed to the coin. "I'll trade my new frog toy for that coin," said Cleo. "It has a coil that makes it hop."

"It's a deal," said T-Bone.

Cleo was rolling the coin when Clifford came by. *Squeak! Squeak!* He was playing with the toy he got from T-Bone.

"That looks like fun," said Cleo. "Would you like to trade your squeaky toy for this coin?"

Clifford looked at the coin. "I traded this coin with T-Bone," Clifford said. "I bet he didn't like playing with it. I'll trade with you, Cleo. I like the coin." So the trade was made.

Clifford had a good time playing with the coin.

While Clifford was playing, Ms. Lee, the librarian, walked by. She stopped to watch. Suddenly, the coin fell and rolled to her feet. Ms. Lee picked it up. "Why, this coin is very valuable," Ms. Lee told Clifford. "It was made long, long ago. I'd like to put it into the museum."

"Would that be okay with you, Clifford?" she asked.

Clifford nodded and wagged his tail.

That very day, Ms. Lee and Clifford brought the coin to Birdwell Island Museum. The coin went into the museum for everyone to see.